Literacy Puzzle Book

Crosswords,
spello-grams,
word games …
and much more

Charles Cripps

Permission to photocopy
This book contains materials which may be reproduced by photocopier or other means for use by the purchaser. The permission is granted on the understanding that these copies will be used within the educational establishment of the purchaser. The book and all its contents remain copyright. Copies may be made without reference to the publisher or the licensing scheme for the making of photocopies operated by the Publishers' Licensing Agency.

Literacy Puzzle Book 1
MT00539
ISBN 978 1 85503 340 5
© Charles Cripps
Illustrations © Anna Curtis
All rights reserved
First published 2001
Reprinted 2002, 2004, 2005, 2007

Printed in the UK for LDA
Abbeygate House, East Road, Cambridge, CB1 1DB, UK

TEACHER'S NOTES

Rationale

The word structure and spelling component of the Primary Framework for Literacy provides teachers with a clearly defined programme for the teaching of spelling. In both the Foundation Stage and Year 1 the teaching of spelling is heavily geared to the teaching of phonics. There is also the expectation that most children will learn 'that segmenting words into their constituent phonemes for spelling is the reverse of blending phonemes into words for reading'. In other words, phonics for reading is not the same as phonics for spelling. Clearly, in the early developmental stages of spelling children are reproducing auditory images. The danger, however, is that many children become so dependent on this 'sounding out' strategy that they remain 'phonic spellers' throughout their schooling. These are also the children who experience difficulty in acquiring the necessary visual strategies that are expected by Year 3.

Obviously, children must be able to hear and discriminate letter sounds, but spelling cannot be caught simply by listening to the sounds in words because the nature of English spelling is such that we can have more than one spelling for the same sound. For spelling it is important that visual skills are promoted from as early as possible and it is for this reason that the puzzles in *Literacy Puzzle Book 1* promote both the auditory and the visual aspects of the spelling system. In *Literacy Puzzle Book 2* the puzzles focus more and more on the visual aspect of learning to spell.

By working through these books children will gradually build up a 'phonic map' of English. They will be made aware that in English the same sound can have different spellings (e.g. b<u>e</u>d and s<u>ai</u>d) and the same spelling can have different sounds (e.g. b<u>o</u>ne, g<u>o</u>ne and d<u>o</u>ne).

Design of the books

Learning to spell must be seen as fun. These books are designed to help children enjoy playing with words and having fun with them. Each puzzle page is designed to enable the teacher to use it with the whole class, a group or with individual children, within or outside a literacy session. The puzzles will also be a useful support for other spelling material based on the visual approach.

The pronunciation used in this material follows the system of the International Phonetic Alphabet (IPA) and is based on the pronunciation associated especially with southern England (sometimes called 'Received Pronunciation').

The mute 'r' is used in puzzles involving vowel phonemes. That is, the 'ɜr' in 'w<u>or</u>k' is used as a single phoneme and not as two separate sounds.

When children are writing words they must be encouraged to write them from memory, thus promoting the 'look-say-cover-write-check' technique.

The words on each puzzle page are based on the phonic elements as described in the Primary Framework for Literacy. Additional phonic elements are included where the spelling is the same but with a different sound. For example, **ear** as in '**near-bear-heard-heart**'. The puzzles also incorporate the kind of words used most frequently in children's writing, many of which have irregular or difficult spellings.

The pages in each book are not arranged in order of difficulty. This enables the teacher to select different pages to meet the individual needs of children.

Change **cat** to **dad**		Change **did** to **this**	
Change the **c** to an **m** =		Change the last **d** to a **g** =	
Change the **m** to **th** =		Change the **d** to a **b** =	
Change the **th** to an **f** =		Change the **g** to a **t** =	
Change the **f** to an **s** =		Change the **b** to an **s** =	
Change the **s** to an **h** =		Change the **s** to an **l** =	
Change the **h** to a **b** =		Change the **l** to an **h** =	
Change the **t** to **ck** =		Change the **t** to an **m** =	
Change the **ck** to a **d** =		Change the **m** to an **s** =	
Change the **b** to a **d** =		Change the **h** to **th** =	

Jump over every other letter to find a new word.

d e o s g = dog   g i o h t = got

y o e t s = yes   l a e j g = ley

m a u l m = mum   n e o m t = not

b o u p t = but   t o h i e s m = thiem

m o u n d = mud   t i h e t d s = this

r s a i n = ran   t e h o a s t = thut

1

Make the new words.

Instead of **h** in **h**en write | men | pen | ten | then

Instead of **m** in **m**et write | get | let | net | pet

Instead of **r** in **r**ed write | bed | f | led | w

Instead of **f** in **f**at write | cat | m | ch | that

Instead of **h** in **h**ut write | but | cut | nut | shut

How many words can you find?

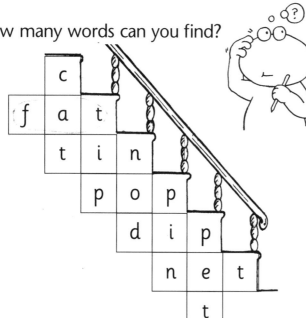

sat

tin

pop

cat

nod

ping

net

pet

tip

Write the four words in each grid.

b	e	d
u		o
n	o	t

bed
ban
dot
not

p	a	t
o		i
t	e	n

pat
pot
ten
tin

th	a	t
a		i
n	a	p

that
tip
than
nap

th	e	m
e		a
n	e	t

then
them
net
mat

Finish the puzzles. Each answer ends with **ack**, **eck**, **ick**, **ock** or **uck**.

you can carry things in one

a young hen

not at the front

you can wear one on your foot

it joins your head to your body

a sign that an answer is right

the opposite of thin

he went up the hill with Jill

a home for a ship

the opposite of white

a bird that swims

Use the code to find out the words.

a	b	c	d	e	f	g	h	i	j	k	l	m
Z	Y	X	W	V	U	T	S	R	Q	P	O	N

n	o	p	q	r	s	t	u	v	w	x	y	z
M	L	K	J	I	H	G	F	E	D	C	B	A

P	R	X	P
k	i	c	k

Y	Z	X	P

M	V	X	P

O	F	X	P

H	L	X	P

K	R	X	P

3

Finish the puzzle.

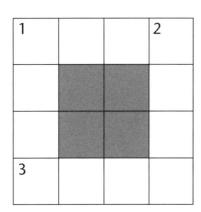

Across

1   throw

3   to make full

Down

1   quarrel

2   opposite of buy

Add double **ll** and then write the whole word.

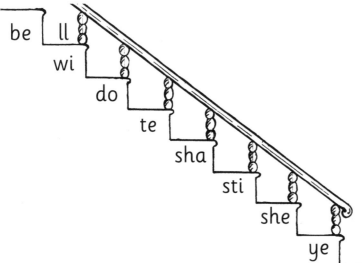

be | ll   bell

wi

do

te

sha

sti

she

ye

Add double **ss** and then write the whole word.

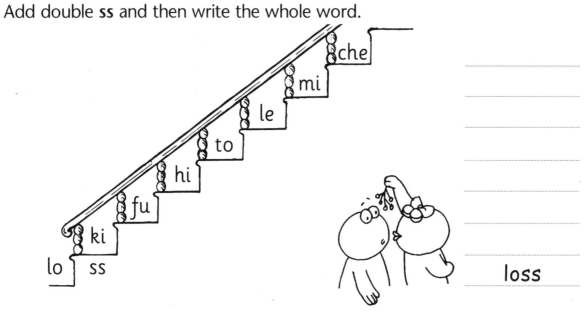

che

mi

le

to

hi

fu

ki

lo | ss   **loss**

Find the double **ff** word. | o | f | o | f | f | i | f | _____

Make words ending in **ang**, **ing**, **ong** and **ung**.

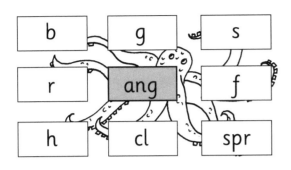

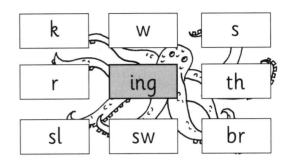

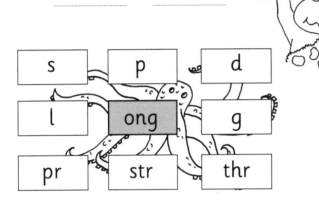

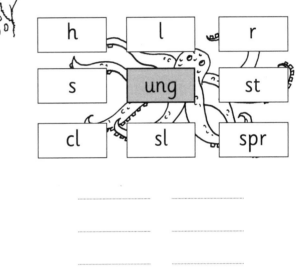

Sort out the jumbled **ng** words.

nigr

gnsa

rognts

gsnu

gwnsi

ugnts

psngar

gnol

rbgni

Write the jumbled words and draw a ring around the answer.

		yes	no
Do **ishf** live in milk?		yes	no
Can you play in a football **amcht**?		yes	no
Can you **iswh** on a star?		yes	no
Can a **shid** swim?		yes	no
Does **ithfl** also mean dirt?		yes	no
Can you **hctac** a ball?		yes	no

Jump over every other letter to find a new word.

m i u s c t h = ☐   s t u e c p h = ☐

w a i n t c h = ☐   r o i e c s h = ☐

c o a l s s h = ☐   r a a y s t h = ☐

m o o n t l h = ☐   h e u o s g h = ☐

Catch a petal and make a flower. Then write your words.

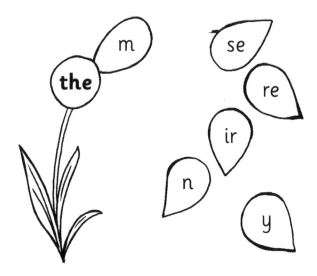

the   m   se   re   ir   n   y

....

....

....

....

....

black	bled	brick	brush
clap	clock	crack	crop
flag	flat	frog	from
glad	glum	grab	grin
plan	plug	pram	prod

Write each word into a pattern shape below. Some shapes may be the same.

Take away the word meaning **sad** and you are left **happy**.

a   m   g   l   g   d   u   l

Cross out one of the letters that appear twice in each grid and make new words.
They all begin with a blend from the box.

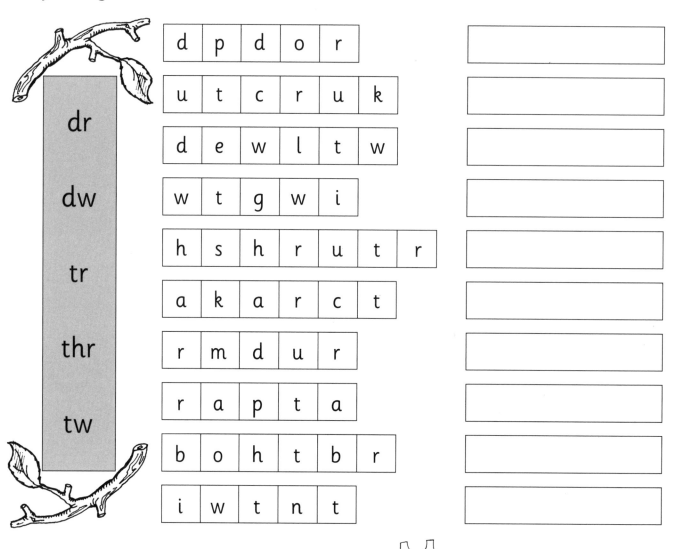

| d | p | d | o | r | |

| u | t | c | r | u | k |

| d | e | w | l | t | w |

| w | t | g | w | i |

| h | s | h | r | u | t | r |

| a | k | a | r | c | t |

| r | m | d | u | r |

| r | a | p | t | a |

| b | o | h | t | b | r |

| i | w | t | n | t |

dr

dw

tr

thr

tw

Finish these words by using a vowel.

| t | r | | t |

| t | w | | g |

| t | h | r | | b |

| d | r | | m |

| t | w | | n |

| d | r | | s | s |

Can you make a word using each ending? Choose one of the openings in the boxes for each. It is possible to do them all.

sc	ell	eck
scr	ash	it
shr	ep	uck
sk	ug	ab
sl	osh	ing
sm	ill	ish
sn	in	an
sp	ong	ed
spl	ap	ack
spr	ang	ung
squ	ip	ub
st	iff	id
str	im	ot
sw	ap	am

scab

My score

and	send	pond	held	help
think	tank	sink	bench	lunch
jump	damp	limp	shelf	golf
milk	silk	desk	risk	crisp

Write each word into a pattern shape below. Some shapes may be the same.

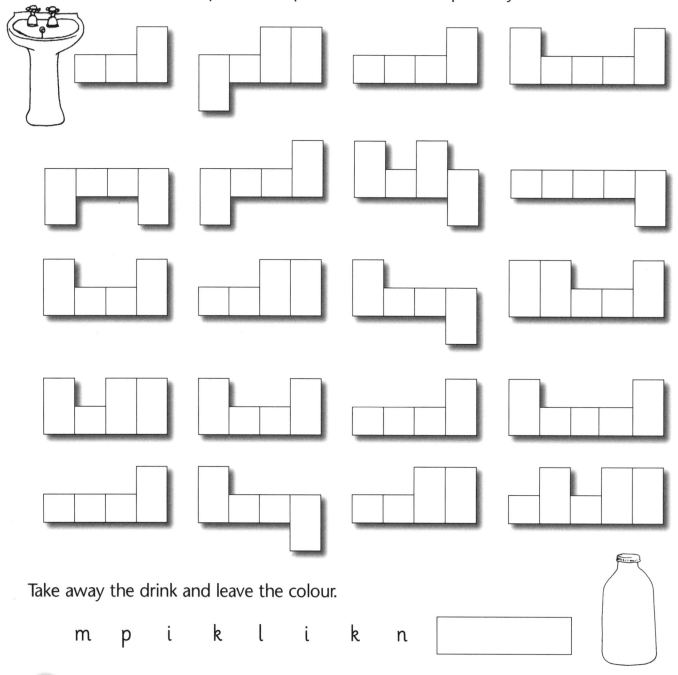

Take away the drink and leave the colour.

m   p   i   k   l   i   k   n

PUZZLE 11 Short vowels and final blends **st, nt, ft, lt, ct, pt** and **xt**

How many words can you make by adding one or more of these endings?

ft	st	nt	lt	xt	ct	pt

be	
fa	
fro	
ju	just
ke	
le	
mu	
ne	
so	
spe	
stri	
swe	
te	
we	

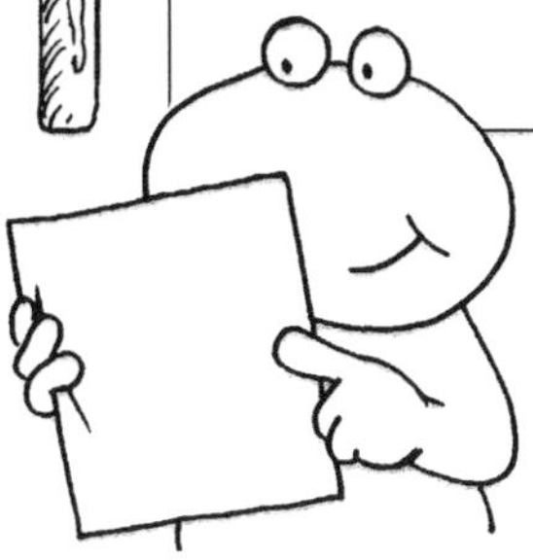

My score

Fill in the words below.

These words end in **st**.

sethc

ttwsi

cstru

stofr

These words end in **mp**.

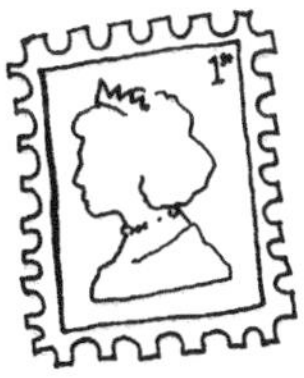

asmpt

mpchi

tspum

uthpm

These words end in **nd**.

ahnd

enpsd

ebldn

asndt

a	e	i	o	u
1	2	3	4	5

Use the code to make words.

c	1	m	e

m	1	d	e

h	4	m	e

t	5	b	e

m	1	k	e

f	3	v	e

w	h	3	t	e

t	3	m	e

t	1	k	e

n	3	n	e

n	1	m	e

l	3	k	e

c	5	b	e

t	h	2	s	e

The insect is pointing to words
beginning with **fire**.
Write these words in the boxes.
Three words need a hyphen.

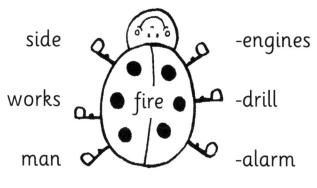

side

works

man

fire

-engines

-drill

-alarm

Finish the spello-gram.

My first is in **came** but not in **same**.

My second is in **lake** but not in **like**.

My third is in **kite** but not in **bite**.

My fourth is in **pipe** but not in **pip**.   What food am I?

Take a letter or a letter pattern from each column to make words.

How many words did you find?

Use the numbers to make new words.

m	a	d	e	=	d	a	m	e
1	2	3	4		3	2	1	4

m	a	t	e	=				
1	2	3	4		3	2	1	4

n	a	m	e	=				
1	2	3	4		3	2	1	4

l	i	f	e	=				
1	2	3	4		3	2	1	4

l	a	t	e	=				
1	2	3	4		3	2	1	4

s	t	o	v	e	=					
1	2	3	4	5		4	3	2	5	1

t	a	k	e	s	=					
1	2	3	4	5		5	3	2	1	4

s	l	o	p	e	=					
1	2	3	4	5		4	3	2	5	1

s	m	i	l	e	=					
1	2	3	4	5		2	3	4	5	1

s	t	o	n	e	=					
1	2	3	4	5		4	3	2	5	1

Finish the **old** puzzles.

the opposite of young

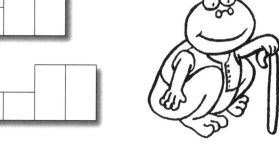

not hot

a bright yellow colour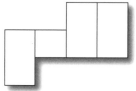

the baker ... me a bun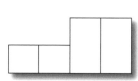

keeping something in your hands + *ing*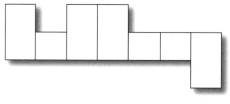

bending paper + *ing*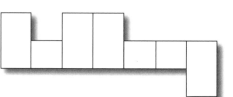

Jump over every other letter to find a new word.

f e i p n o d = ☐   k u i b n e d = ☐

w o i s l k d = ☐   m o i g n i d = ☐

b a i f n g d = ☐   m a i l l a d = ☐

c t h l i a l e d e r n e l n = ☐

Use **ay** or **ai** to finish the words on the snail.

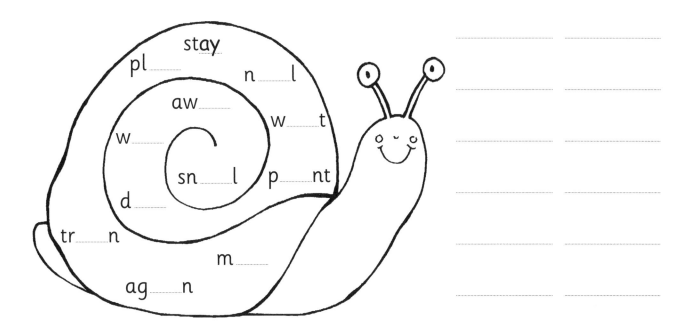

Use **i, y, ie** or **igh** to finish the words on the cloud.

Take the sound of **a** as in t**a**ke and change it to the sound of **i** as in f**i**ve.
Remember we are changing the sounds and the spellings will need to change.

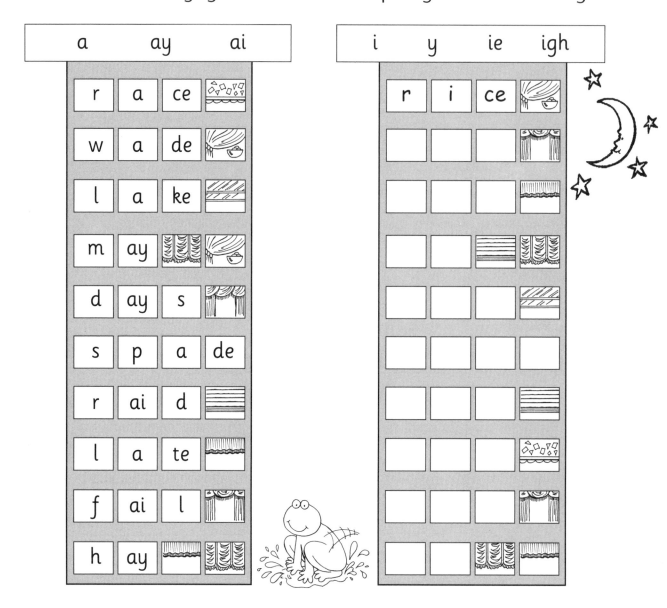

Match the words with their clues.

fight	light	might	night	right	tight

to row and argue ⬜   do not turn left, turn ... ⬜

my boots are too ⬜   not day, but ... ⬜

we ... do it ⬜   not dark, but ... ⬜

Use **ee** or **ea** to finish the words on the sheep.

leaf   b___n   l___p   gr___n   s___   tr___   s___   m___l   thr___   s___t   b___n   h___t   t___ch   s___n

Take the sound of **e** as in **me** and change it to the sound of **i** as in **five**.
Remember we are changing the sounds and the spellings will need to change.

e	ee	ea
m	e	
h	e	
b	ee	
s	ee	
b	ea	k
m	ee	t
t	r	ee
r	ea	d
w	ee	p

i	y	ie	igh
m	y		

Use **ow** or **oa** to finish the words on the boat.

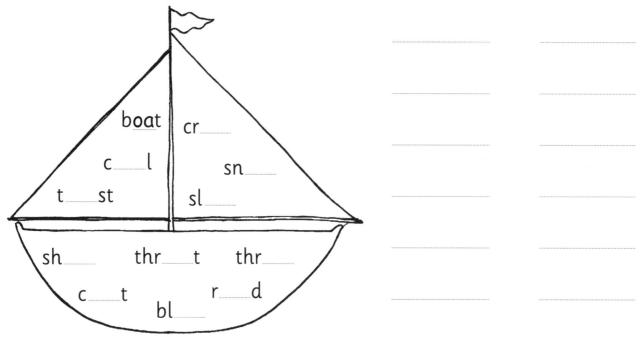

boat
cr.........
c.......l
sn.........
t.......st
sl.........
sh.........
thr.......t
thr.........
c.......t
r.......d
bl.........

Take the sound of **o** as in **go** and change it to the sound of **a** as in **take**.
Remember we are changing the sounds and the spellings will need to change.

o	ow	oa
l	ow	
m	ow	
r	oa	d
l	oa	d
s	t	o	ne
w	o	ke
f	oa	l
g	oa	t
b	r	o	ke

a	ay	ai
l	ay	

Cross out letters to leave a two-letter word.

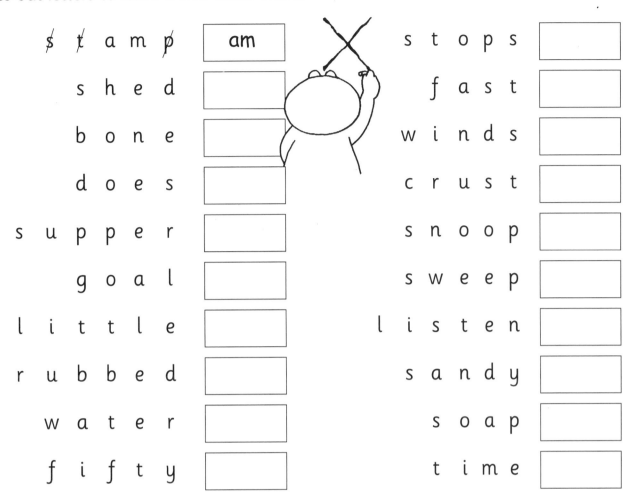

s̸ t̸ a m p̸	am	s t o p s
s h e d		f a s t
b o n e		w i n d s
d o e s		c r u s t
s u p p e r		s n o o p
g o a l		s w e e p
l i t t l e		l i s t e n
r u b b e d		s a n d y
w a t e r		s o a p
f i f t y		t i m e

In these sentences the words have been joined together.
Write them again, leaving spaces between the words.

Wewillgototheparkandplayontheswings.

....

PatandIwillbehomeintimefortea.

....

Doyouknowifthebushasgone?

....

Ihopewewillbeintimefortheparty.

....

Finish the pattern.

	+ s	+ ed	+ ing
book	books	booked	booking
	cooks		
		hooked	
			looking

Finish the sums.

b + ook + s = ☐   b + ook + ing = ☐

l + ook + ed = ☐   l + ook + ing = ☐

c + ook + s = ☐   c + ook + ed = ☐

h + ook + ing = ☐   h + ook + ed = ☐

Jump over letters to find a new word.

t e o f o e k = ☐   p l u n t = ☐

p l u s l h l = ☐   g r o a o d d = ☐

h e o d o c k = ☐   p l u n s t h = ☐

s s t r o p o e d = ☐

Can you decode these sentences? The vowels (a – e – i – o – u) are missing.

Th* g*rl h*d t*k*n *ll h*r b**ks t* sch**l.

....

S*m t**k th* c*rt fr*m th* sh*d *nd p*sh*d *t h*m*.

....

Write out the coded message.

 can c u in the car.

....

Y did u spill t on my jam tart?

....

 would like 2 know when u r coming 2 c my new farm.

....

When will the 4 of u b home from the park?

....

Finish the pattern.

	+ s	+ ed	+ ing
bark	barks	barked	barking
	harms		
		parked	
			parting
blast			
	grasps		
		lasted	
			clasping

Cross out one of the letters that appear twice and make a new word.

̷k s t a l	last	
k s b a s		
s m a t t		
c f a r c t		

b a h t b	
t a f s s	
p a t p s	
a r c h n h	

Finish the puzzles.

b
t
j ——— oy
R
enj

b
c
s ——— oil
t
sp

Finish the pattern.

	+ s	+ ed	+ ing
boil	boils	boiled	boiling
	spoils		
		joined	
			pointing

Finish the puzzle.

b + oi + l + s = ☐   p + oi + nt + ed = ☐

sp + oi + l + ing = ☐   b + oi + l + ing = ☐

j + oi + n + ing = ☐   j + oi + n + s = ☐

sp + oi + l + ed = ☐

p + oi + nt + ing = ☐

south	found	down	mouse	few	new

Use the words above to finish the puzzles.

in is to **out** as
up is to ⬚

east is to **west** as
north is to ⬚

left is to **right** as
lost is to ⬚

hot is to **cold** as
old is to ⬚

hard is to **soft** as
many is to ⬚

geese is to **goose**
as **mice** is to ⬚

Can you decode these sentences? The vowels (a – e – i – o – u) are missing.

Th* *ld h**s* w*s m*d* **t *f r*d br*cks.

T*m w*s n*w f*v* y**rs *ld.

H*w m*ny d*ys *n * w**k?

Th* t*m* *s *b**t s*x *'cl*ck.

Add **ow** and then write the whole word.

br
s
r
n
h
b
c | ow

cow

Use **oo**, **ew** or **ue** to finish the words in the boot.

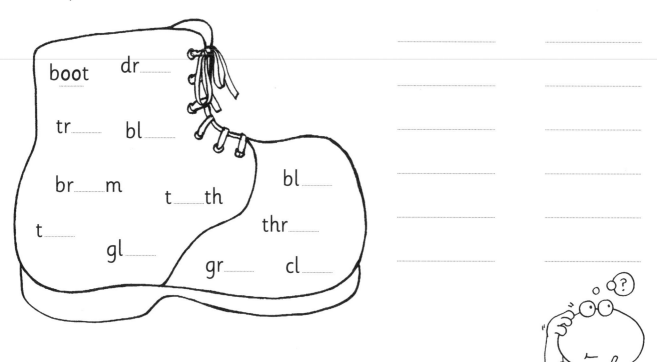

boot   dr……

tr……   bl……

br……m   t……th   bl……

t……   thr……

gl……

gr……   cl……

Can you find the words in the word square?

t	o	o	t	h	o	o	s
l	i	c	l	u	e	c	k
s	o	o	b	o	o	t	e
e	b	l	u	e	e	n	d
g	r	e	b	r	o	o	m
e	t	r	u	e	w	e	d
b	u	e	g	r	e	w	t
a	g	l	u	e	g	o	m

the baby grew his first ...

you need one when doing a puzzle

you can wear one

a colour

sweep the floor with one

the opposite of false

Sam ...10 cm last year

used to stick things together

Write the sounds of each word in a box.

room

r	oo	m

drew

true

threw

tooth

food

broom

glues

Write the word with the same
sound but different spelling.

Finish the puzzles.

fair

bare

wear

there

stair

hare

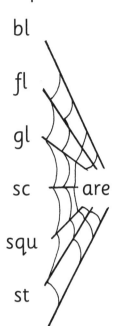

bl

fl

gl

sc ——— are

squ

st

c

Use the code to find out the words.

a	b	c	d	e	f	g	h	i	j	k	l	m
Z	Y	X	W	V	U	T	S	R	Q	P	O	N

n	o	p	q	r	s	t	u	v	w	x	y	z
M	L	K	J	I	H	G	F	E	D	C	B	A

X	Z	I	V
c	a	r	e

S	Z	R	I

D	S	V	I	V

U	Z	R	I

D	V	Z	I

G	S	V	R	I

K	V	Z	I

K	Z	R	I

X	S	Z	R	I

Y	V	Z	I

W	Z	I	V

G	S	V	I	V

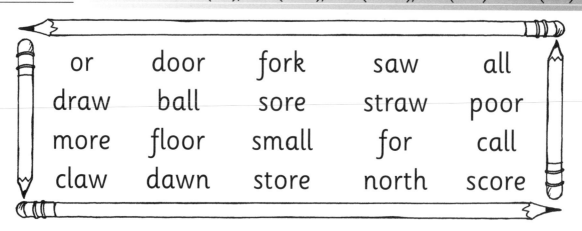

or	door	fork	saw	all
draw	ball	sore	straw	poor
more	floor	small	for	call
claw	dawn	store	north	score

Write each word into a pattern shape below. Some shapes may be the same.

Take away the time of day and leave the bouncing toy.

l   b   d   l   w   n   a   a

Can you make a word using each ending? Chose one of the
openings in the boxes for each. It is possible to do them all.

b	
c	
d	
f	
g	
h	
j	
n	
p	
s	
t	
v	
w	
ch	

urn	urve
ir	erm
orse	ere
urse	erse
er	ur
irp	url
ird	irl
urst	ork
erch	urnt
urly	irst
erd	urt
urch	erk
orm	irt
erve	ord

burn

My score

Find the smaller words in the long word.

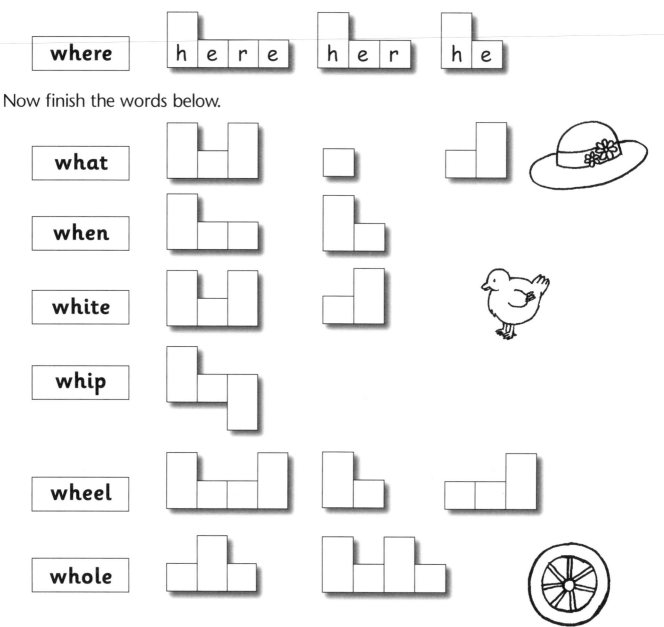

| where | h e r e | h e r | h e |

Now finish the words below.

| what |
| when |
| white |
| whip |
| wheel |
| whole |

Write the following words in their question box.

| hand | never | house | her | them | under | she | pie |
| behind | yesterday | near | today | you | clock | soon | above |

where	when	what	who
?	?	?	?

Finish the pattern.

	+ s	double the final letter + ed	+ ing
wag	wags	wagged	wagging
	rubs		
		nodded	
			humming
pin			
	taps		

Finish the puzzle.

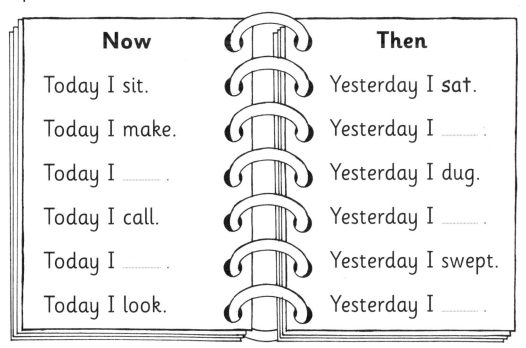

Now		**Then**
Today I sit.		Yesterday I sat.
Today I make.		Yesterday I _____.
Today I _____.		Yesterday I dug.
Today I call.		Yesterday I _____.
Today I _____.		Yesterday I swept.
Today I look.		Yesterday I _____.

Finish the pattern.

	+ s	+ ed	+ ing
fill	fills	filled	filling
	calls		
		pulled	
			puffing

Draw a circle around the **ch** which sounds different from the rest.

chat   such   chin   Christmas

Draw a square around the **ch** which sounds different from the rest.

chip   school   chop   church

Finish the sums.

t + a + lk = ☐   t + a + lk + ed = ☐

t + a + lk + s = ☐   w + a + lk + s = ☐

w + a + lk = ☐   w + a + lk + ed = ☐

t + a + lk + ing = ☐   st + a + lk = ☐

ch + a + lk = ☐   w + a + lk + ing = ☐

Write each word into a pattern shape below.

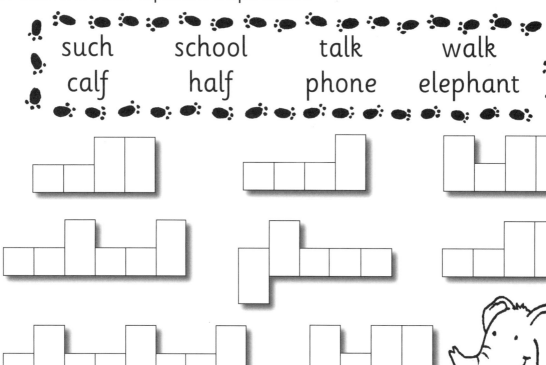

such   school   talk   walk
calf   half   phone   elephant

Write these words into their own **ear** sound box.

dear	heard	bear	
pear	hear	wear	
fear	earn	year	learn
near	heart	tear	clear
early	spear	gear	earth

dear	earth	bear

Which word needs a box of its own?

Finish the sums.

y + ear + ly = [ ]   d + ear + ly = [ ]

n + ear + ly = [ ]   cl + ear + ly = [ ]

31

Use each beginning and each ending once only to make different **ea** words.

Beginnings   Endings

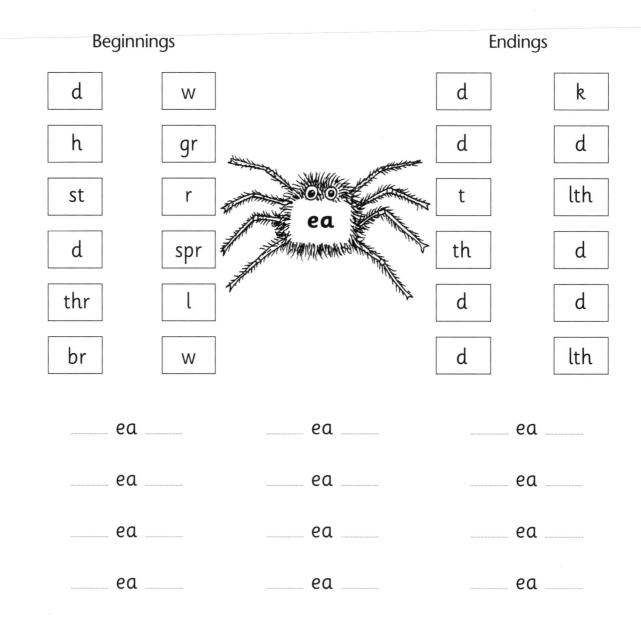

d	w
h	gr
st	r
d	spr
thr	l
br	w

d	k
d	d
t	lth
th	d
d	d
d	lth

.... ea .... ea .... ea ....

.... ea .... ea .... ea ....

.... ea .... ea .... ea ....

.... ea .... ea .... ea ....

Finish the **ea** puzzle.

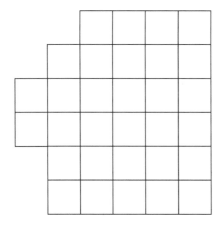

on your shoulders	wealth
used to make a sandwich	great
a lot of money	bread
put butter on bread	steak
if you enjoy something it is	spread
often cooked on a barbecue	head

Finish the puzzles.

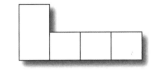 = 60 minutes

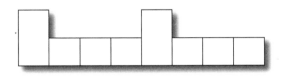 = red is one and so is blue

= one more than thirteen

 = not mine

= used to make bread

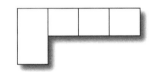 = ... water into a cup from a jug

Finish the sentences with **our** words.

_____ house is around the next corner.

Is that _____ house over there?

One before five is _____ .

Sugar is sweet but lemons are _____ .

Make **ood** words.

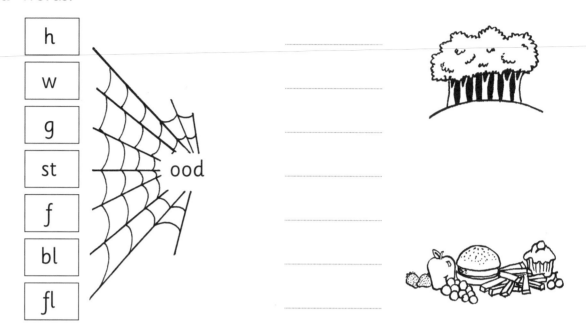

h
w
g
st
f
bl
fl

ood

Finish the puzzles.

happy is to **sad** as
bad is to ⬚

is is to **are** as
was is to ⬚

will is to **won't** as
can is to ⬚

him is to **her** as
he is to ⬚

found is to **lost** as
down is to ⬚

clean is to **dirty** as
open is to ⬚

Trace over the trails to make the words. Each trail must go through the **oo** box.

....

Make **ful** words.

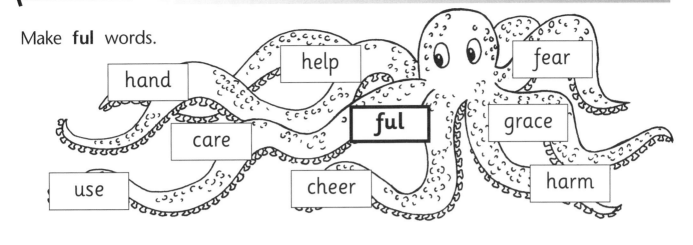

....

....

Begin at the top and find the eight words.
The last letter of one word must always begin the next word.

....

....

....

....

This time write the eight words in the grid.
The last letter of one word must always begin the next word.

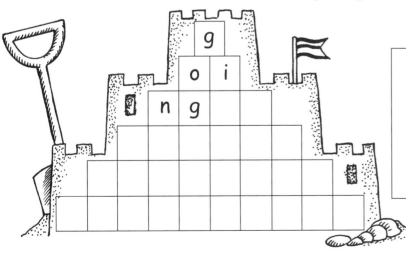

grapes	girl
live	eat
said	running
going	their

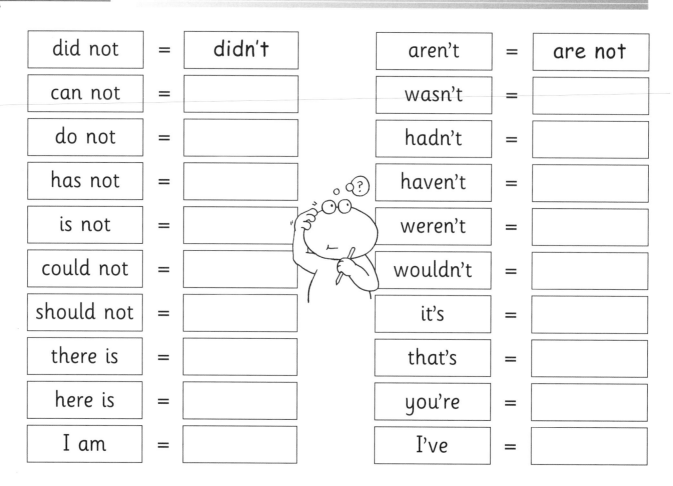

did not	=	didn't	
can not	=		
do not	=		
has not	=		
is not	=		
could not	=		
should not	=		
there is	=		
here is	=		
I am	=		

aren't	=	are not
wasn't	=	
hadn't	=	
haven't	=	
weren't	=	
wouldn't	=	
it's	=	
that's	=	
you're	=	
I've	=	

Finish the crossword by using the contraction of each clue.
Use a separate square for each apostrophe.

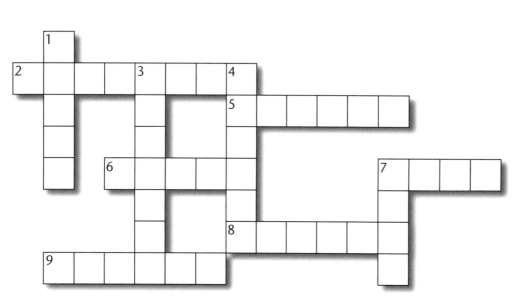

Across

2. could not
5. has not
6. is not
7. I have
8. she will
9. what is

Down

1. do not
3. does not
4. that is
7. I will

Write these words into their own sound box for the letter **a**.

and	last	than	was	came	had
make	back	after	called	has	any
want	water	can	all	made	ball
name	man	many	have	call	can't
ran	half	that	what	dad	take

and

last

came

what

any

all

Sort out the jumbled letters.

eavh ☐

twna ☐

retfa ☐

kame ☐

nhta ☐

rewta ☐

flah ☐

dallec ☐

naym ☐

Listen to the vowel sound of **o** in each of the following words.

one	once

The letter **o** makes the same sound as **wu**. | **o = wu** |

Now write these words into their own sound box for the letter **o**.

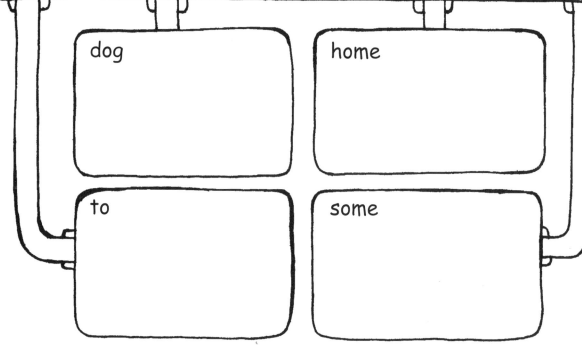

dog	home	some	do	over	of
to	old	got	don't	come	going
off	another	two	no	not	love
so	from	brother	go	who	on

dog

home

to

some

Can you decode the beginning of this story? The vowels (a – e – i – o – u) have been left out.

nc *p*n * t*m* *v*r *n* h*ndr*d y**rs *g*

Write these words into their same vowel sound box.

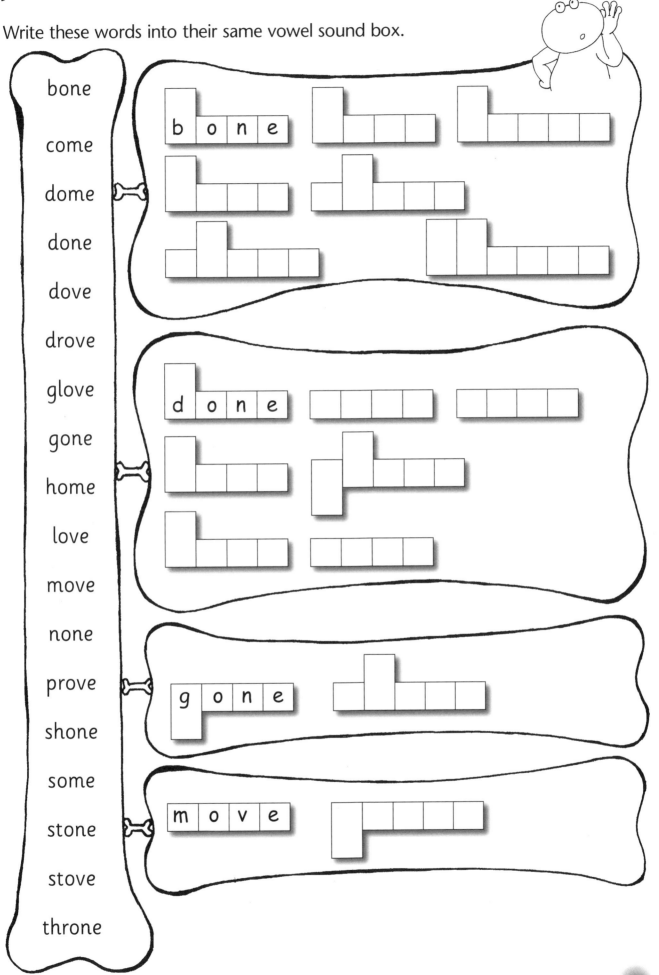

bone

come

dome

done

dove

drove

glove

gone

home

love

move

prove

shone

some

stone

stove

throne

Look at our mystery consonant.

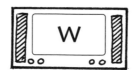

Listen to the vowel sound. Write the sounds of each word in a box.

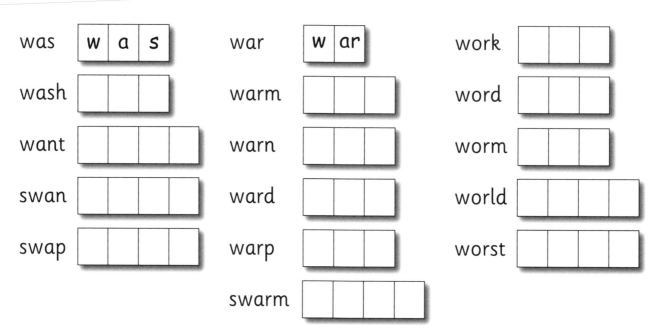

was | w | a | s

war | w | ar

work

wash

warm

word

want

warn

worm

swan

ward

world

swap

warp

worst

swarm

Use the letters **a**, **ar** or **or** to make words.

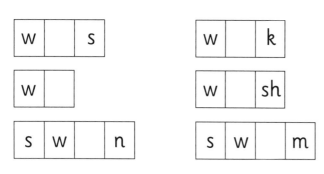

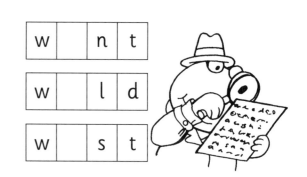

In these sentences the words have been joined together.
Write them again, leaving spaces between the words.

Thesunwasshininganditwasverywarminsidetheclassroom.

....

Theteacherhadtogiveawordofwarningaboutplayingontheroad.

....

Latiflikedtolearntospellthenamesofallthecountriesintheworld.

....

Find the smaller words in the long word.

| that | h a t | a | a t |

Now finish the words below.

| what |

| then |

| when |

| there |

| where |

| some |

| many |

These two questions are written backwards. Can you match the answers?

| The time is 4 o'clock. | | There are seven. |

?keew a ni syad ynam woH

?emit eht si tahW

Find the smaller words in the long word.

there	here her he

Now finish the words below.

them
water
down
mother
father
brother
another

Sort out these jumbled sentences.

week. on is next My holiday going brother

_____

her father my train. catch My to mother took

_____

is dry tonight. I need The it very to garden water so will

_____

there Jo another said would tonight. be storm that

_____

tree. help from pet the Julie down her to cat tried

_____

Write the word with the different spelling for the vowel sound.

meal — seat — team — been —   **been**

seen — queen — people — speed —

laugh — park — hard — cart —

sport — water — torn — storm —

hood — foot — shook — should —

was — wash — because — want —

night — like — nine — hide —

truck — spun — come — cut —

what — shop — spot — rock —

stood — would — good — wood —

Find the correct spellings and write them out.

| wuns | wot | very | sed |
| once | what | verey | said |

| could | becos | laugh | meny |
| cood | because | larf | many |

Reverse the order of these sounds and write the new word.

| p | o | t |

| t | a | p |

| t | e | n |

| t | u | b |

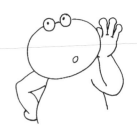

| t | o | p |

| | | |

| | | |

| | | |

Remember we are reversing sounds and the spellings may need to change.

| t | u | ck |

| c | u | t |

| l | i | ck |

| k | i | ll |

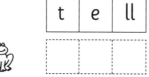

| t | e | ll |

| | | |

| sh | a | ck |

| | | |

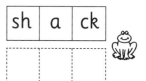

| k | i | ss |

| | | |

| l | e | ss |

| | | |

| s | k | i | p |

| | | | |

| s | t | a | ck |

| | | | |

| m | a | ke |

| | | |

| s | a | fe |

| | | |

| s | k | a | te |

| | | | |

| s | t | o | ne |

| | | | |

| l | a | te |

| | | |

| l | i | fe |

| | | |

| s | l | o | pe |

| | | | |

| s | c | a | le |

| | | | |

| l | oa | f |

| | | |

| d | ie | s |

| | | |

| s | p | ea | k |

| | | | |

| s | n | ai | l |

| | | | |

| p | oo | l |

| | | |

| c | oo | k |

| | | |

| m | igh | t |

| | | |

| s | l | igh | t |

| | | | |

| ch | ar | m |

| | | |

| ch | ir | p |

| | | |

| ch | ur | ch |

| | | |

| v | er | se |

| | | |

Listen carefully to the underlined sound in the following word pairs.
Are they the same or different? Trace over the right answer.

| s**ai**d / p**ai**d | same   different | g**o**ing / d**o**ing | same   different |

| th**ere** / b**ear** | same   different | h**ou**se / d**ow**n | same   different |

| w**ere** / **ear**ly | same   different | **are** / c**are** | same   different |

| s**aw** / sm**a**ll | same   different | b**u**t / p**u**t | same   different |

| sh**ou**ld / sh**ou**t | same   different | f**a**ther / gr**a**ss | same   different |

| bu**s** / ha**s** | same   different | ta**lk** / ba**ke** | same   different |

| s**ch**ool / **ch**op | same   different | **wh**en / **wh**o | same   different |

| ha**lf** / o**ff** | same   different | **ph**one / **f**irst | same   different |

Each day is mixed up. Write them out correctly.
Do not forget to begin each word with a capital letter.

n m o

day

_____

s t a r u

day

_____

r f i

day

_____

h r u t s

day

_____

d e s n e w

day

_____

s e u t

day

_____

n u s

day

_____

Finish the sentences. Each dash means a letter.

Last T___day it rained, but not on Wed___day.

We will be in London next Sat__day and S__day.

It is Pat's birthday on M__day.

Can you come over to my house next Th___day or F__day?

PUZZLE 47   Numbers

Write down the ten number words hidden in this bag. The words go across and down.

....

....

....

t	t	w	o	b	o	u	e
a	m	i	n	e	n	t	i
t	e	s	e	v	e	n	g
h	o	m	t	c	f	b	h
r	e	a	d	i	s	f	t
e	t	y	d	e	s	i	x
e	e	n	i	n	e	v	c
p	n	o	g	i	x	e	e
f	o	u	r	e	s	y	l

Write out the coded numbers.

a	1
b	2
c	3
d	4
e	5
f	6
g	7
h	8
i	9
j	10
k	11
l	12
m	13
n	14
o	15
p	16
q	17
r	18
s	19
t	20
u	21
v	22
w	23
x	24
y	25
z	26

5	12	5	22	5	14

5	9	7	8	20	5	5	14

20	23	5	14	20	25

6	15	21	18	20	5	5	14

19	5	22	5	14	20	5	5	14

20	8	9	18	20	5	5	14

19	9	24	20	5	5	14

6	9	6	20	5	5	14

20	23	5	12	22	5

14	9	14	5	20	5	5	14

Which colours are we mixing?

e u l b

_____

d r e

_____

e n g r e

_____

k a c l b

_____

n i p k

_____

w y l o l e

_____

h w e i t

_____

r u p p e l

_____

w n o r b

_____

Begin at the top and find the eight words.
The last letter of one word must always begin the next word.

Change **cat** to **dad**		Change **did** to **this**	
Change the **c** to an **m** =	mat	Change the last **d** to a **g** =	dig
Change the **m** to **th** =	that	Change the **d** to a **b** =	big
Change the **th** to an **f** =	fat	Change the **g** to a **t** =	bit
Change the **f** to an **s** =	sat	Change the **b** to an **s** =	sit
Change the **s** to an **h** =	hat	Change the **s** to an **l** =	lit
Change the **h** to a **b** =	bat	Change the **l** to an **h** =	hit
Change the **t** to **ck** =	back	Change the **t** to an **m** =	him
Change the **ck** to a **d** =	bad	Change the **m** to an **s** =	his
Change the **b** to a **d** =	dad	Change the **h** to **th** =	this

Jump over every other letter to find a new word.

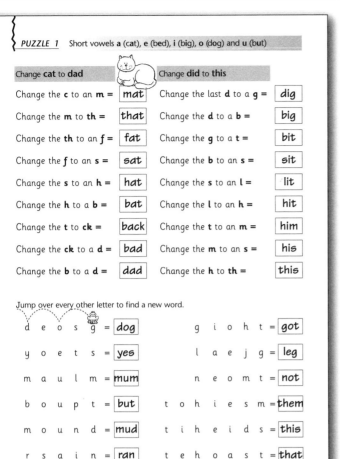

d e o s g =	dog	g i o h t =	got
y o e t s =	yes	l a e j g =	leg
m a u l m =	mum	n e o m t =	not
b o u p t =	but	t o h i e s m =	them
m o u n d =	mud	t i h e i d s =	this
r s a i n =	ran	t e h o a s t =	that

Make the new words.

Instead of **h** in **h**en write	men	pen	ten	then
Instead of **m** in **m**et write	get	let	net	pet
Instead of **r** in **r**ed write	bed	fed	led	wed
Instead of **f** in **f**at write	cat	mat	chat	that
Instead of **h** in **h**ut write	but	cut	nut	shut

How many words can you find?

```
      c
  f a t
    t i n
        p o p
          d i p
            n e t
    t
```

fat	cat
tin	tip
pop	nod
dip	pin
net	pet

Write the four words in each grid.

b	e	d
u		o
n	o	t

p	a	t
o		i
o	t	e	n

th	a	t
a		i
n	a	p

th	e	m
e		a
n	e	t

bed	pat	that	them
dot	tin	tip	mat
bun	pot	than	then
not	ten	nap	net

Finish the puzzles. Each answer ends with **ack**, **eck**, **ick**, **ock** or **uck**.

you can carry things in one	sack
a young hen	chick
not at the front	back
you can wear one on your foot	sock
it joins your head to your body	neck
a sign that an answer is right	tick
the opposite of thin	thick
he went up the hill with Jill	Jack
a home for a ship	dock
the opposite of white	black
a bird that swims	duck

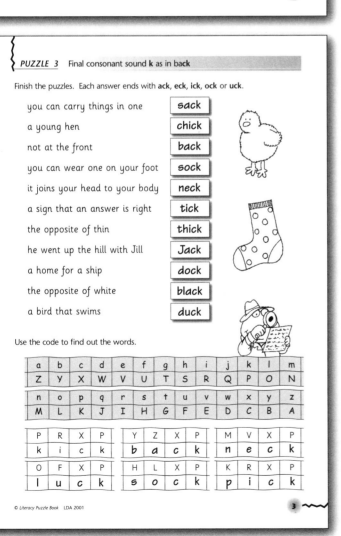

Use the code to find out the words.

a	b	c	d	e	f	g	h	i	j	k	l	m
Z	Y	X	W	V	U	T	S	R	Q	P	O	N

n	o	p	q	r	s	t	u	v	w	x	y	z
M	L	K	J	I	H	G	F	E	D	C	B	A

P	R	X	P		Y	Z	X	P		M	V	X	P
k	i	c	k		b	a	c	k		n	e	c	k

O	F	X	P		H	L	X	P		K	R	X	P
l	u	c	k		s	o	c	k		p	i	c	k

Finish the puzzle.

¹t	o	s	²s
i			e
f			l
³f	i	l	l

Across
1   throw
3   to make full

Down
1   quarrel
2   opposite of buy

Add double **ll** and then write the whole word.

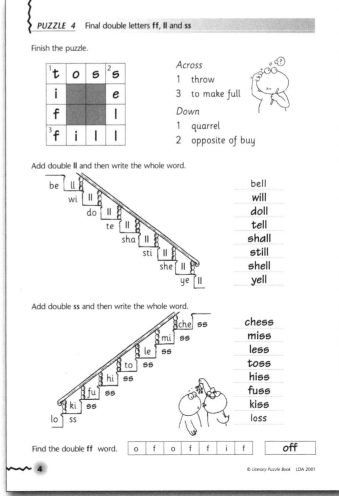

be ll	bell
wi ll	will
do ll	doll
te ll	tell
sha ll	shall
sti ll	still
she ll	shell
ye ll	yell

Add double **ss** and then write the whole word.

che ss	chess
mi ss	miss
le ss	less
to ss	toss
hi ss	hiss
fu ss	fuss
ki ss	kiss
lo ss	loss

Find the double **ff** word.

o	f	o	f	f	i	f		off

Make words ending in **ang**, **ing**, **ong** and **ung**.

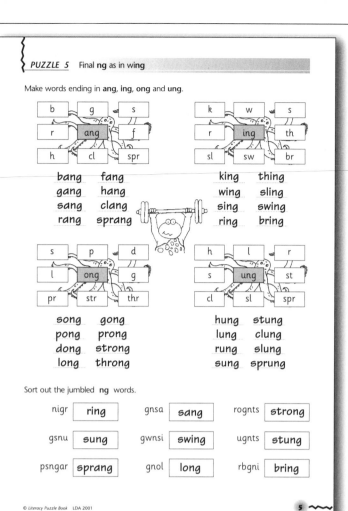

b	g	s
r	ang	f
h	cl	spr

k	w	s
r	ing	th
sl	sw	br

bang   fang
gang   hang
sang   clang
rang   sprang

king   thing
wing   sling
sing   swing
ring   bring

s	p	d
l	ong	g
pr	str	thr

h	l	r
s	ung	st
cl	sl	spr

song   gong
pong   prong
dong   strong
long   throng

hung   stung
lung   clung
rung   slung
sung   sprung

Sort out the jumbled **ng** words.

nigr	**ring**	gnsa	**sang**	rognts	**strong**
gsnu	**sung**	gwnsi	**swing**	ugnts	**stung**
psngar	**sprang**	gnol	**long**	rbgni	**bring**

5

~ 6

Write the jumbled words and draw a ring around the answer.

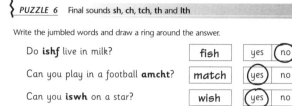
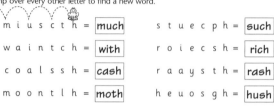

Do **ishf** live in milk?   fish   yes   (no)

Can you play in a football **amcht**?   match   (yes)   no

Can you **iswh** on a star?   wish   (yes)   no

Can a **shid** swim?   dish   yes   (no)

Does **ithfl** also mean dirt?   filth   (yes)   no

Can you **hctac** a ball?   catch   (yes)   no

Jump over every other letter to find a new word.

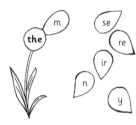

m i u s c t h = **much**   s t u e c p h = **such**

w a i n t c h = **with**   r o i e c s h = **rich**

c o a l s s h = **cash**   r a a y s t h = **rash**

m o o n t l h = **moth**   h e u o s g h = **hush**

Catch a petal and make a flower. Then write your words.

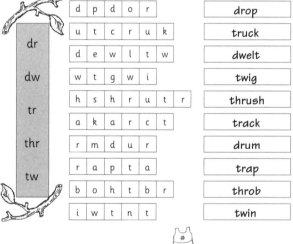

the   m   se   re   ir   n   y

them
these
there
their
then
they

black	bled
clap	clock
flag	flat
glad	glum
plan	plug

brick	brush
crack	crop
frog	from
grab	grin
pram	prod

Write each word into a pattern shape below. Some shapes may be the same.

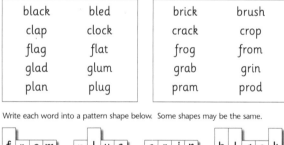
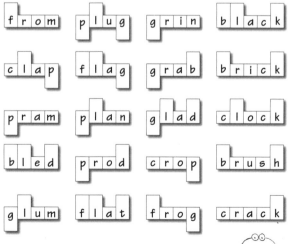

from   plug   grin   black

clap   flag   grab   brick

pram   plan   glad   clock

bled   prod   crop   brush

glum   flat   frog   crack

Take away the word meaning **sad** and you are left **happy**.

a m g l g d u l   **glad**

7 ~

~ 8

Cross out one of the letters that appear twice in each grid and make new words.
They all begin with a blend from the box.

dr				

d	p	d	o	r
u	t	c	r	u	k
d	e	w	l	t	w
w	t	g	w	i
h	s	h	r	u	t	r
a	k	a	r	c	t
r	m	d	u	r
r	a	p	t	a
b	o	h	t	b	r
i	w	t	n	t

dr
dw
tr
thr
tw

drop
truck
dwelt
twig
thrush
track
drum
trap
throb
twin

Finish these words by using a vowel.

| t | r | o | t | | t | w | i | g | | t | h | r | o | b |

trot   twig   throb

| d | r | u | m | | t | w | i | n | | d | r | e | s | s |

drum   twin   dress

~ 8

Can you make a word using each ending? Choose one of the openings in the boxes for each. It is possible to do them all.

sc		ell	eck		smell	speck
scr		ash	it		smash	split
shr		ep	uck		step	struck
sk		ug	ab		shrug	scab
sl		osh	ing		splosh	spring
sm		ill	ish		still	squish
sn		in	an		skin	scan
sp		ong	ed		strong	shred
spl		ap	ack		scrap	snack
spr		ang	ung		sprang	swung
squ		ip	ub		skip	scrub
st		iff	id		sniff	squid
str		im	ot		slim	spot
sw		ap	am		slap	swam

My score

9

---

and	send	pond	held	help
think	tank	sink	bench	lunch
jump	damp	limp	shelf	golf
milk	silk	desk	risk	crisp

Write each word into a pattern shape below. Some shapes may be the same.

a n d   g o l f   s e n d   b e n c h

j u m p   p o n d   h e l p   c r i s p

t a n k   m i l k   d a m p   t h i n k

h e l d   d e s k   s i n k   l u n c h

r i s k   l i m p   s i l k   s h e l f

Take away the drink and leave the colour.

m p i k l i k n   pink

How many words can you make by adding one or more of these endings?

Fill in the words below.

ft	st	nt	lt	xt	ct	pt

be	best bent belt
fa	fact
fro	frost
ju	just
ke	kept
le	left lent
mu	must
ne	nest next
so	soft
spe	spent spelt
stri	strict
swe	swept
te	test tent text
we	went west wept

These words end in **st**.

sethc	chest
ttwsi	twist
cstru	crust
stofr	frost

These words end in **mp**.

asmpt	stamp
mpchi	chimp
tspum	stump
uthpm	thump

These words end in **nd**.

ahnd	hand
enpsd	spend
ebldn	blend
asndt	stand

My score

11

---

a	e	i	o	u
1	2	3	4	5

Use the code to make words.

c 1 m e	came		t 3 m e	time
m 1 d e	made		t 1 k e	take
h 4 m e	home		n 3 n e	nine
t 5 b e	tube		n 1 m e	name
m 1 k e	make		l 3 k e	like
f 3 v e	five		c 5 b e	cube
w h 3 t e	white		t h 2 s e	these

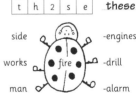

The insect is pointing to words beginning with **fire**.
Write these words in the boxes.
Three words need a hyphen.

side -engines
works fire -drill
man -alarm

fireside	fireworks	fireman
fire-engines	fire-drill	fire-alarm

Finish the spello-gram.

My first is in **came** but not in **same**.
My second is in **lake** but not in **like**.
My third is in **kite** but not in **bite**.
My fourth is in **pipe** but not in **pip**.   What food am I?   cake

12

Take a letter or a letter pattern from each column to make words.

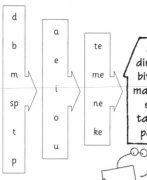

date dame dane dime
dine dome dune duke bake
bite bike bone mate mane
make mime mine mike mute
spite spine spike spoke
tame take time tone tune
pane pine pike poke puke

How many words did you find?

Use the numbers to make new words.

m a d e	=	d a m e
1 2 3 4		3 2 1 4

m a t e	=	t a m e
1 2 3 4		3 2 1 4

n a m e	=	m a n e
1 2 3 4		3 2 1 4

l i f e	=	f i l e
1 2 3 4		3 2 1 4

l a t e	=	t a l e
1 2 3 4		3 2 1 4

s t o v e	=	v o t e s
1 2 3 4 5		4 3 2 5 1

t a k e s	=	s k a t e
1 2 3 4 5		5 3 2 1 4

s l o p e	=	p o l e s
1 2 3 4 5		4 3 2 5 1

s m i l e	=	m i l e s
1 2 3 4 5		2 3 4 5 1

s t o n e	=	n o t e s
1 2 3 4 5		4 3 2 5 1

© Literacy Puzzle Book   LDA 2001   **13**

Finish the **old** puzzles.

the opposite of young   o l d

not hot   c o l d

a bright yellow colour   g o l d

the baker ... me a bun   s o l d

keeping something in your hands + *ing*   h o l d i n g

bending paper + *ing*   f o l d i n g

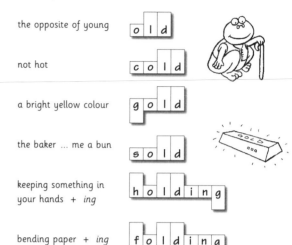

Jump over every other letter to find a new word.

f e i p n o d = **find**   k u i b n e d = **kind**

w o i s l k d = **wild**   m o i g n i d = **mind**

b a i f n g d = **bind**   m a i l l a d = **mild**

c t h l i a l e d e r n e l n = **children**

14   © Literacy Puzzle Book   LDA 2001

Use **ay** or **ai** to finish the words on the snail.

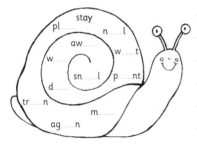

stay	nail
play	wait
paint	way
away	snail
again	may
day	train

Use **i, y, ie** or **igh** to finish the words on the cloud.

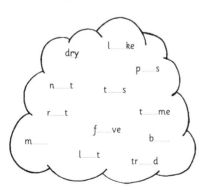

dry	like
night	pies
ties	right
time	my
light	tried
five	by

© Literacy Puzzle Book   LDA 2001   **15**

Take the sound of **a** as in **take** and change it to the sound of **i** as in **five**.
Remember we are changing the sounds and the spellings will need to change.

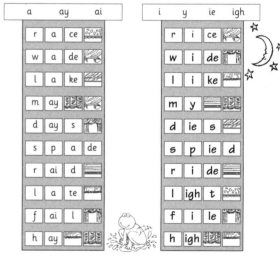

Match the words with their clues.

fight	light	might	night	right	tight

to row and argue   **fight**   do not turn left, turn ...   **right**

my boots are too   **tight**   not day, but ...   **night**

we ... do it   **might**   not dark, but ...   **light**

16   © Literacy Puzzle Book   LDA 2001

Use **ee** or **ea** to finish the words on the sheep.

leaf	been
leap	see
three	heat
meal	green
teach	seen
seat	tree
sea	been

Take the sound of **e** as in **me** and change it to the sound of **i** as in **five**.
Remember we are changing the sounds and the spellings will need to change.

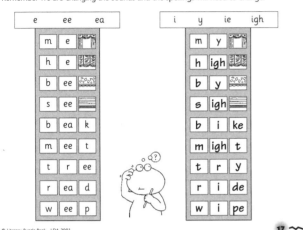

e	ee	ea

m	e	
h	e	
b	ee	
s	ee	
b	ea	k
m	ee	t
t	r	ee
r	ea	d
w	ee	p

i	y	ie	igh

m	y	
h	igh	
b	y	
s	igh	
b	i	ke
m	igh	t
t	r	y
r	i	de
w	i	pe

Use **ow** or **oa** to finish the words on the boat.

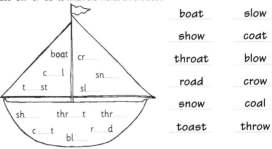

boat	slow
show	coat
throat	blow
road	crow
snow	coal
toast	throw

Take the sound of **o** as in **go** and change it to the sound of **a** as in **take**.
Remember we are changing the sounds and the spellings will need to change.

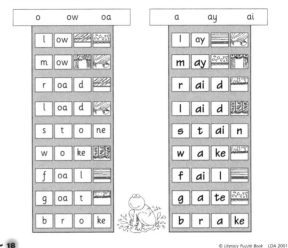

o	ow	oa

l	ow	
m	ow	
r	oa	d
l	oa	d
s	t	o	ne
w	o	ke
f	oa	l
g	oa	t
b	r	o	ke

a	ay	ai

l	ay	
m	ay	
r	ai	d
l	ai	d
s	t	ai	n
w	a	ke
f	ai	l
g	a	te
b	r	a	ke

Cross out letters to leave a two-letter word.

s t a m p	am	s t o p s	to
s h e d	he	f a s t	as
b o n e	on	w i n d s	in
d o e s	do	c r u s t	us
s u p p e r	up	s n o o p	no
g o a l	go	s w e e p	we
l i t t l e	it	l i s t e n	is
r u b b e d	be	s a n d y	an
w a t e r	at	s o a p	so
f i f t y	if	t i m e	me

In these sentences the words have been joined together.
Write them again, leaving spaces between the words.

Wewillgototheparkandplayontheswings.

We will go to the park and play on the swings.

PatandIwillbehomeintimefortea.

Pat and I will be home in time for tea.

Doyouknowifthebushasgone?

Do you know if the bus has gone?

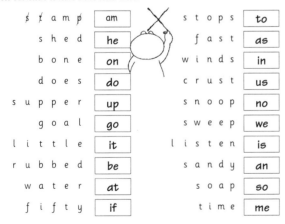

Ihopewewillbeintimefortheparty.

I hope we will be in time for the party.

Finish the pattern.

	+ s	+ ed	+ ing
book	books	booked	booking
cook	cooks	cooked	cooking
hook	hooks	hooked	hooking
look	looks	looked	looking

Finish the sums.

b + ook + s = **books**   b + ook + ing = **booking**

l + ook + ed = **looked**   l + ook + ing = **looking**

c + ook + s = **cooks**   c + ook + ed = **cooked**

h + ook + ing = **hooking**   h + ook + ed = **hooked**

Jump over letters to find a new word.

t e o f o e k = **took**   p l u n t = **put**

p l u s l h l = **pull**   g r o a o d d = **good**

h e o d o c k = **hook**   p l u n s t h = **push**

s s t r o p o e d = **stood**

Can you decode these sentences? The vowels (a – e – i – o – u) are missing.

Th* g*rl h*d t*k*n *ll h*r b**ks t* sch**l.

The girl had taken all her books to school.

S*m t**k th* c*rt fr*m th* sh*d *nd p*sh*d *t h*m*.

Sam took the cart from the shed and pushed it home.

Write out the coded message.

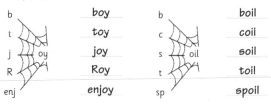

👁 can c u in the car.
I can see you in the car.

Y did u spill t on my jam tart?
Why did you spill tea on my jam tart?

👁 would like 2 know when u r coming 2 c my new farm.
I would like to know when you are coming to see my new farm.

When will the 4 of u b home from the park?
When will the four of you be home from the park?

Finish the pattern.

	+ s	+ ed	+ ing
bark	barks	barked	barking
harm	harms	harmed	harming
park	parks	parked	parking
part	parts	parted	parting
blast	blasts	blasted	blasting
grasp	grasps	grasped	grasping
last	lasts	lasted	lasting
clasp	clasps	clasped	clasping

Cross out one of the letters that appear twice and make a new word.

l s t a l	**last**	b a h t b	**bath**
k s b a s	**bask**	t a f s s	**fast**
s m a t t	**mast**	p a t p s	**past**
c f a r c t	**craft**	a r c h n h	**ranch**

21

Finish the puzzles.

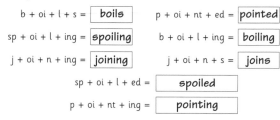

b	**boy**
t	**toy**
j	**joy**
R	**Roy**
enj	**enjoy**

b	**boil**
c	**coil**
s	**soil**
t	**toil**
sp	**spoil**

Finish the pattern.

	+ s	+ ed	+ ing
boil	boils	boiled	boiling
spoil	spoils	spoiled	spoiling
join	joins	joined	joining
point	points	pointed	pointing

Finish the puzzle.

b + oi + l + s = **boils**   p + oi + nt + ed = **pointed**

sp + oi + l + ing = **spoiling**   b + oi + l + ing = **boiling**

j + oi + n + ing = **joining**   j + oi + n + s = **joins**

sp + oi + l + ed = **spoiled**

p + oi + nt + ing = **pointing**

22

| south | found | down | mouse | few | new |

Use the words above to finish the puzzles.

in is to **out** as
up is to **down**

east is to **west** as
north is to **south**

left is to **right** as
lost is to **found**

hot is to **cold** as
old is to **new**

hard is to **soft** as
many is to **few**

geese is to **goose**
as **mice** is to **mouse**

Can you decode these sentences? The vowels (a – e – i – o – u) are missing.

Th* *ld h**s* w*s m*d* **t *f r*d br*cks.
The old house was made out of red bricks.

T*m w*s n*w f*v* y**rs *ld.
Tom was now five years old.

H*w m*ny d*ys *n * w**k?
How many days in a week?

Th* t*m* *s *b**t s*x *'cl*ck.
The time is about six o'clock.

Add **ow** and then write the whole word.

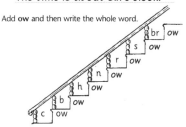

br ow   **brow**
s ow   **sow**
r ow   **row**
n ow   **now**
h ow   **how**
b ow   **bow**
c ow   **cow**

23

Use **oo**, **ew** or **ue** to finish the words in the boot.

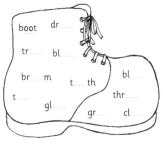

boot	**drew**
true	**broom**
blue	**blew**
too	**glue**
tooth	**grew**
clue	**threw**

Can you find the words in the word square?

t	o	o	t	h	o	o	s
l	i	c	l	u	e	c	k
s	o	o	b	o	o	t	e
e	b	l	u	e	e	n	d
g	r	e	b	r	o	o	m
e	t	r	u	e	w	e	d
b	u	e	g	r	e	w	t
a	g	l	u	e	g	o	m

the baby grew his first ...
you need one when doing a puzzle
you can wear one
a colour
sweep the floor with one
the opposite of false
Sam ...10 cm last year
used to stick things together

Write the sounds of each word in a box.

room	r	oo	m		tooth	t	oo	th
drew	d	r	ew		food	f	oo	d
true	t	r	ue		broom	b	r	oo	m
threw	th	r	ew		glues	g	l	ue	s

24

54

PUZZLE 25   Vowel sound air (hair), are (care), ere (there), eir (their) and ear (wear)

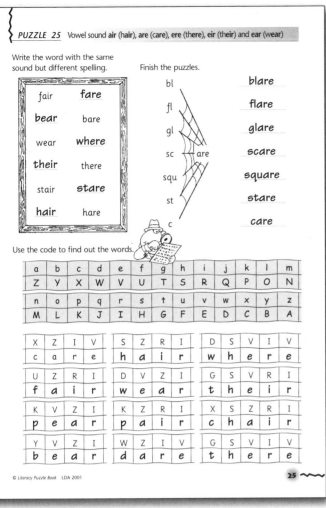

Write the word with the same sound but different spelling.

fair	**fare**
bear	bare
wear	**where**
their	there
stair	**stare**
hair	hare

Finish the puzzles.

bl ___ **blare**
fl ___ **flare**
gl ___ **glare**
sc ___ are **scare**
squ ___ **square**
st ___ **stare**
c ___ **care**

Use the code to find out the words.

a	b	c	d	e	f	g	h	i	j	k	l	m
Z	Y	X	W	V	U	T	S	R	Q	P	O	N

n	o	p	q	r	s	t	u	v	w	x	y	z
M	L	K	J	I	H	G	F	E	D	C	B	A

X Z I V	S Z R I	D S V I V
c a r e	h a i r	w h e r e

U Z R I	D V Z I	G S V R I
f a i r	w e a r	t h e i r

K V Z I	K Z R I	X S Z R I
p e a r	p a i r	c h a i r

Y V Z I	W Z I V	G S V I V
b e a r	d a r e	t h e r e

25

PUZZLE 26   Vowel sound or (for), oor (door), ore (more), aw (saw) and a (ball)

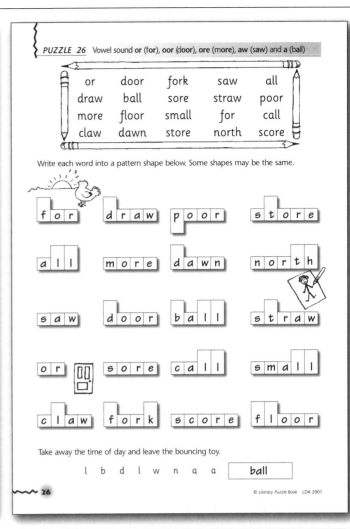

or	door	fork	saw	all
draw	ball	sore	straw	poor
more	floor	small	for	call
claw	dawn	store	north	score

Write each word into a pattern shape below. Some shapes may be the same.

f o r   d r a w   p o o r   s t o r e

a l l   m o r e   d a w n   n o r t h

s a w   d o o r   b a l l   s t r a w

o r   s o r e   c a l l   s m a l l

c l a w   f o r k   s c o r e   f l o o r

Take away the time of day and leave the bouncing toy.

l   b   d   l   w   n   a   a   **ball**

26

PUZZLE 27   Vowel sound er (her), ere (were), ir (bird), or (word) and ur (turn)

Can you make a word using each ending? Chose one of the openings in the boxes for each. It is possible to do them all.

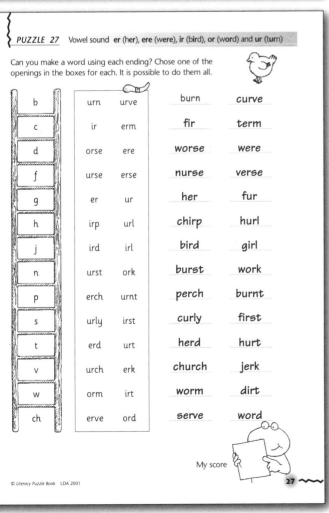

b	urn	urve
c	ir	erm
d	orse	ere
f	urse	erse
g	er	ur
h	irp	url
j	ird	irl
n	urst	ork
p	erch	urnt
s	urly	irst
t	erd	urt
v	urch	erk
w	orm	irt
ch	erve	ord

burn	curve
fir	term
worse	were
nurse	verse
her	fur
chirp	hurl
bird	girl
burst	work
perch	burnt
curly	first
herd	hurt
church	jerk
worm	dirt
serve	word

My score

27

PUZZLE 28   Different sounds for wh (what) (who)

Find the smaller words in the long word.

| where | h e r e | h e r | h e |

Now finish the words below.

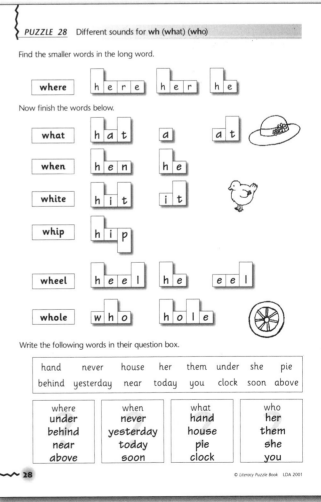

what	h a t	a	a t
when	h e n	h e	
white	h i t	i t	
whip	h i p		
wheel	h e e l	h e	e e l
whole	w h o	h o l e	

Write the following words in their question box.

| hand | never | house | her | them | under | she | pie |
| behind | yesterday | near | today | you | clock | soon | above |

where	when	what	who
under	never	hand	her
behind	yesterday	house	them
near	today	pie	she
above	soon	clock	you

28

Finish the pattern.

	+ s	double the final letter	
		+ ed	+ ing
wag	wags	wagged	wagging
rub	rubs	rubbed	rubbing
nod	nods	nodded	nodding
hum	hums	hummed	humming
pin	pins	pinned	pinning
tap	taps	tapped	tapping

Finish the puzzle.

Now	Then
Today I sit.	Yesterday I sat.
Today I make.	Yesterday I made.
Today I dig.	Yesterday I dug.
Today I call.	Yesterday I called.
Today I sweep.	Yesterday I swept.
Today I look.	Yesterday I looked.

Finish the pattern.

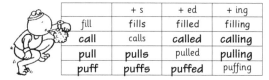

	+ s	+ ed	+ ing
fill	fills	filled	filling
call	calls	called	calling
pull	pulls	pulled	pulling
puff	puffs	puffed	puffing

Draw a circle around the **ch** which sounds different from the rest.

chat   such   chin   (Christmas)

Draw a square around the **ch** which sounds different from the rest.

chip   s[ch]ool   chop   church

Finish the sums.

t + a + lk =	talk	t + a + lk + ed =	talked
t + a + lk + s =	talks	w + a + lk + s =	walks
w + a + lk =	walk	w + a + lk + ed =	walked
t + a + lk + ing =	talking	st + a + lk =	stalk
ch + a + lk =	chalk	w + a + lk + ing =	walking

Write each word into a pattern shape below.

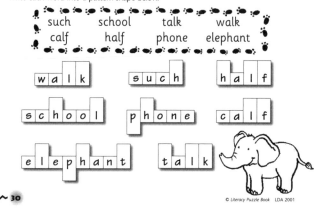

such   school   talk   walk
calf   half   phone   elephant

w a l k   s u c h   h a l f

s c h o o l   p h o n e   c a l f

e l e p h a n t   t a l k

Write these words into their own **ear** sound box.

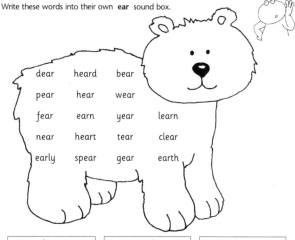

dear   heard   bear
pear   hear   wear
fear   earn   year   learn
near   heart   tear   clear
early   spear   gear   earth

dear	earth	bear
hear fear	heard	pear
near year	earn	wear
clear spear	learn	tear
tear gear	early	

Which word needs a box of its own?   heart

Finish the sums.

| y + ear + ly = | yearly | d + ear + ly = | dearly |
| n + ear + ly = | nearly | cl + ear + ly = | clearly |

Use each beginning and each ending once only to make different **ea** words.

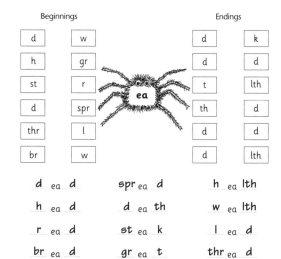

Beginnings

d	w
h	gr
st	r
d	spr
thr	l
br	w

ea

Endings

d	k
d	d
t	lth
th	d
d	lth

d ea d   spr ea d   h ea lth

h ea d   d ea th   w ea lth

r ea d   st ea k   l ea d

br ea d   gr ea t   thr ea d

Finish the **ea** puzzle.

h	e	a	d		on your shoulders
b	r	e	a	d	used to make a sandwich
w	e	a	l	t	h	a lot of money
s	p	r	e	a	d	put butter on bread
g	r	e	a	t	if you enjoy something it is
s	t	e	a	k	often cooked on a barbecue

wealth
great
bread
steak
spread
head

PUZZLE 33 Different sounds for **our** (our) (your) (hour) (colour)

Finish the puzzles.

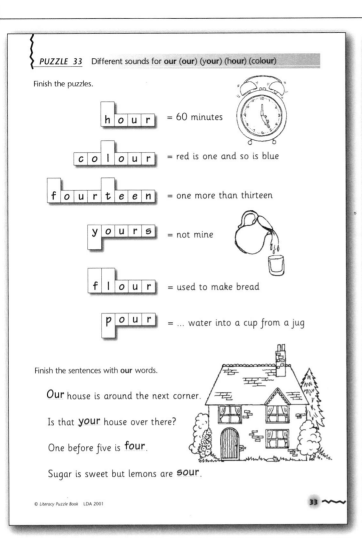

| h | o | u | r | = 60 minutes

| c | o | l | o | u | r | = red is one and so is blue

| f | o | u | r | t | e | e | n | = one more than thirteen

| y | o | u | r | s | = not mine

| f | l | o | u | r | = used to make bread

| p | o | u | r | = ... water into a cup from a jug

Finish the sentences with **our** words.

Our house is around the next corner.

Is that **your** house over there?

One before five is **four**.

Sugar is sweet but lemons are **sour**.

33

PUZZLE 34 Different sounds for **oo** (good) (food) (flood)

Make **ood** words.

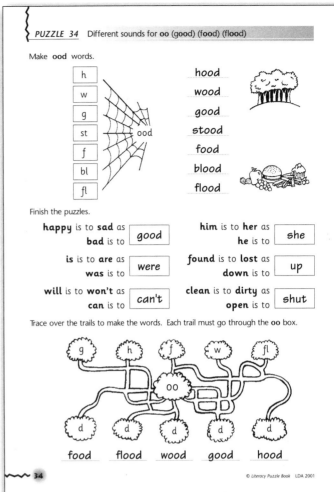

| h |
| w |
| g |
| st |
| f |
| bl |
| fl |

ood

hood
wood
good
stood
food
blood
flood

Finish the puzzles.

happy is to **sad** as
bad is to [good]

is is to **are** as
was is to [were]

will is to **won't** as
can is to [can't]

him is to **her** as
he is to [she]

found is to **lost** as
down is to [up]

clean is to **dirty** as
open is to [shut]

Trace over the trails to make the words. Each trail must go through the **oo** box.

| g | h | f | w | fl |

oo

| d | d | d | d | d |

food   flood   wood   good   hood

34

PUZZLE 35 Mixed words

Make **ful** words.

hand   help   fear
care   **ful**   grace
use   cheer   harm

handful   helpful   fearful   careful

graceful   useful   cheerful   harmful

Begin at the top and find the eight words.
The last letter of one word must always begin the next word.

		v		
	e	r		
y	o	u	n	
t	i	l	i	v	e
d	w	e	l	l	i	t	t
l	e	n	d	s	i	s	t	e	r

very   you
until   lived
dwell   little
ends   sister

This time write the eight words in the grid.
The last letter of one word must always begin the next word.

		g		
	o	i		
	n	g	i	r	
l	i	v	e	a	t
h	e	i	r	u	n	n	i
n	g	r	a	p	e	s	a	i	d

grapes   girl
live   eat
said   running
going   their

35

PUZZLE 36 Contractions

did not	=	didn't
can not	=	can't
do not	=	don't
has not	=	hasn't
is not	=	isn't
could not	=	couldn't
should not	=	shouldn't
there is	=	there's
here is	=	here's
I am	=	I'm

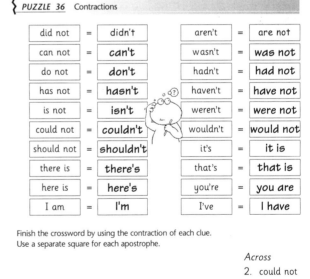

aren't	=	are not
wasn't	=	was not
hadn't	=	had not
haven't	=	have not
weren't	=	were not
wouldn't	=	would not
it's	=	it is
that's	=	that is
you're	=	you are
I've	=	I have

Finish the crossword by using the contraction of each clue.
Use a separate square for each apostrophe.

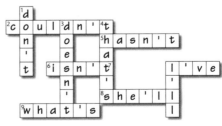

Across
2. could not
5. has not
6. is not
7. I have
8. she will
9. what is

Down
1. do not
3. does not
4. that is
7. I will

36

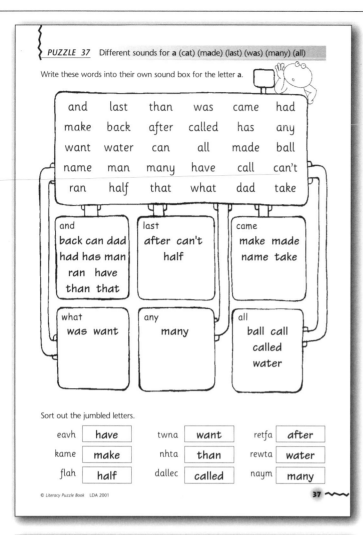

PUZZLE 37 Different sounds for **a** (cat) (made) (last) (was) (many) (all)

Write these words into their own sound box for the letter **a**.

and	last	than	was	came	had
make	back	after	called	has	any
want	water	can	all	made	ball
name	man	many	have	call	can't
ran	half	that	what	dad	take

and — back can dad had has man ran have than that

last — after can't half

came — make made name take

what — was want

any — many

all — ball call called water

Sort out the jumbled letters.

eavh	**have**	twna	**want**	retfa	**after**
kame	**make**	nhta	**than**	rewta	**water**
flah	**half**	dallec	**called**	naym	**many**

© Literacy Puzzle Book LDA 2001

37

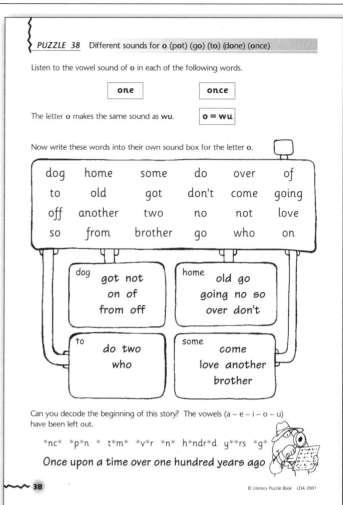

PUZZLE 38 Different sounds for **o** (pot) (go) (to) (done) (once)

Listen to the vowel sound of **o** in each of the following words.

one   **once**

The letter **o** makes the same sound as **wu**.   **o = wu**

Now write these words into their own sound box for the letter **o**.

dog	home	some	do	over	of
to	old	got	don't	come	going
off	another	two	no	not	love
so	from	brother	go	who	on

dog — got not on of from off

home — old go going no so over don't

to — do two who

some — come love another brother

Can you decode the beginning of this story? The vowels (a – e – i – o – u) have been left out.

nc *p*n * t*m* *v*r *n* h*ndr*d y**rs *g*

Once upon a time over one hundred years ago

© Literacy Puzzle Book LDA 2001

38

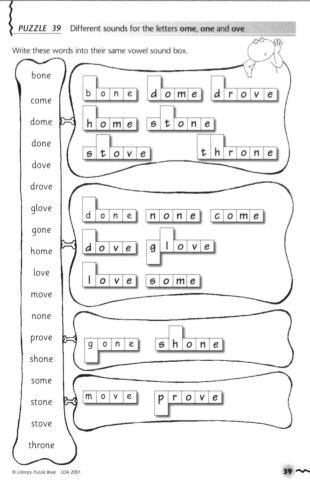

PUZZLE 39 Different sounds for the letters **ome**, **one** and **ove**

Write these words into their same vowel sound box.

bone
come
dome
done
dove
drove
glove
gone
home
love
move
none
prove
shone
some
stone
stove
throne

Box 1: b o n e   d o m e   d r o v e   h o m e   s t o n e   s t o v e   t h r o n e

Box 2: d o n e   n o n e   c o m e   d o v e   g l o v e   l o v e   s o m e

Box 3: g o n e   s h o n e

Box 4: m o v e   p r o v e

© Literacy Puzzle Book LDA 2001

39

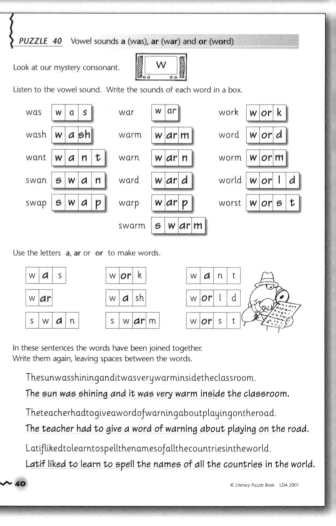

PUZZLE 40 Vowel sounds **a** (was), **ar** (war) and **or** (word)

Look at our mystery consonant.   **w**

Listen to the vowel sound. Write the sounds of each word in a box.

was	w a s	war	w ar	work	w or k
wash	w a sh	warm	w arm	word	w or d
want	w a n t	warn	w arn	worm	w or m
swan	s w a n	ward	w ar d	world	w or l d
swap	s w a p	warp	w ar p	worst	w or s t
		swarm	s w arm		

Use the letters **a**, **ar** or **or** to make words.

w a s	w or k	w a n t
w ar	w a sh	w or l d
s w a n	s w ar m	w or s t

In these sentences the words have been joined together.
Write them again, leaving spaces between the words.

Thesunwasshininganditwasverywarminsidetheclassroom.
The sun was shining and it was very warm inside the classroom.

Theteacherhadtogiveawordofwarningaboutplayingontheroad.
The teacher had to give a word of warning about playing on the road.

Latiflikedtolearntospellthenamesofallthecountriesintheworld.
Latif liked to learn to spell the names of all the countries in the world.

© Literacy Puzzle Book LDA 2001

40

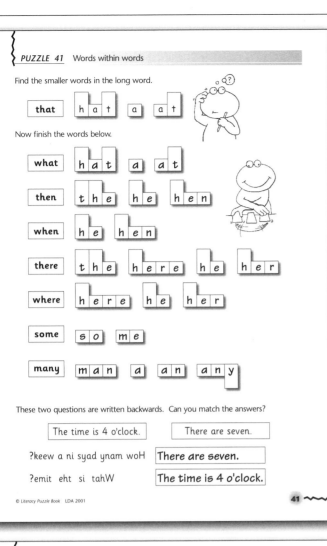

PUZZLE 41   Words within words

Find the smaller words in the long word.

that — h a t | a | a t

Now finish the words below.

what — h a t | a | a t

then — t h e | h e | h e n

when — h e | h e n

there — t h e | h e r e | h e | h e r

where — h e r e | h e | h e r

some — s o | m e

many — m a n | a | a n | a n y

These two questions are written backwards. Can you match the answers?

The time is 4 o'clock.   There are seven.

?keew a ni syad ynam woH   **There are seven.**

?emit eht si tahW   **The time is 4 o'clock.**

41

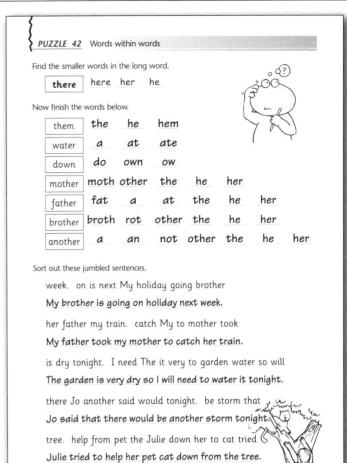

PUZZLE 42   Words within words

Find the smaller words in the long word.

there — here   her   he

Now finish the words below.

them — the   he   hem

water — a   at   ate

down — do   own   ow

mother — moth   other   the   he   her

father — fat   a   at   the   he   her

brother — broth   rot   other   the   he   her

another — a   an   not   other   the   he   her

Sort out these jumbled sentences.

week. on is next My holiday going brother

My brother is going on holiday next week.

her father my train. catch My to mother took

My father took my mother to catch her train.

is dry tonight. I need The it very to garden water so will

The garden is very dry so I will need to water it tonight.

there Jo another said would tonight. be storm that

Jo said that there would be another storm tonight.

tree. help from pet the Julie down her to cat tried

Julie tried to help her pet cat down from the tree.

42

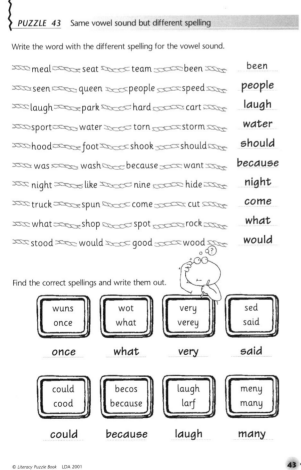

PUZZLE 43   Same vowel sound but different spelling

Write the word with the different spelling for the vowel sound.

meal   seat   team   been   **been**

seen   queen   people   speed   **people**

laugh   park   hard   cart   **laugh**

sport   water   torn   storm   **water**

hood   foot   shook   should   **should**

was   wash   because   want   **because**

night   like   nine   hide   **night**

truck   spun   come   cut   **come**

what   shop   spot   rock   **what**

stood   would   good   wood   **would**

Find the correct spellings and write them out.

| wuns / **once** | wot / **what** | very / verey | sed / **said** |
| **once** | **what** | **very** | **said** |

| could / cood | becos / **because** | **laugh** / larf | meny / **many** |
| **could** | **because** | **laugh** | **many** |

43

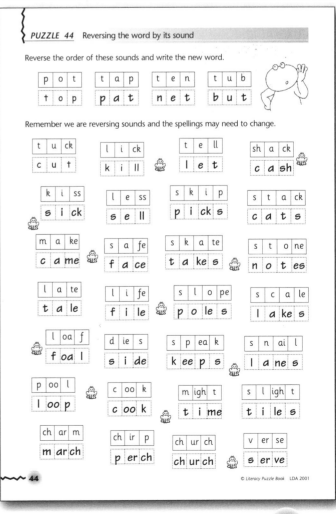

PUZZLE 44   Reversing the word by its sound

Reverse the order of these sounds and write the new word.

p o t → t o p   t a p → p a t   t e n → n e t   t u b → b u t

Remember we are reversing sounds and the spellings may need to change.

t u ck → c u t   l i ck → k i ll   t e ll → l e t   sh a ck → c a sh

k i ss → s i ck   l e ss → s e ll   s k i p → p i ck s   s t a ck → c a t s

m a ke → c a me   s a fe → f a ce   s k a te → t a ke s   s t o ne → n o te s

l a te → t a le   l i fe → f i le   s l o pe → p o le s   s c a le → l a ke s

l oa f → f oa l   d ie s → s i de   s p ea k → k ee p s   s n ai l → l a ne s

p oo l → l oo p   c oo k → c oo k   m igh t → t i me   s l igh t → t i le s

ch ar m → m ar ch   ch ir p → p er ch   ch ur ch → ch ur ch   v er se → s er ve

44

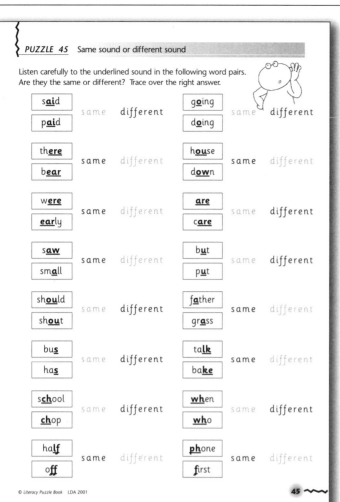

PUZZLE 45 — Same sound or different sound

Listen carefully to the underlined sound in the following word pairs.
Are they the same or different? Trace over the right answer.

s**ai**d / p**ai**d	same	different	g**o**ing / d**o**ing	same	different	
th**ere** / b**ear**	same	different	h**ou**se / d**ow**n	same	different	
w**ere** / **ear**ly	same	different	**are** / c**are**	same	different	
s**aw** / sm**a**ll	same	different	b**u**t / p**u**t	same	different	
sh**ou**ld / sh**ou**t	same	different	**fa**ther / gr**a**ss	same	different	
bu**s** / ha**s**	same	different	ta**lk** / ba**ke**	same	different	
s**ch**ool / **ch**op	same	different	**wh**en / **wh**o	same	different	
ha**lf** / o**ff**	same	different	**ph**one / **f**irst	same	different	

© Literacy Puzzle Book LDA 2001

45

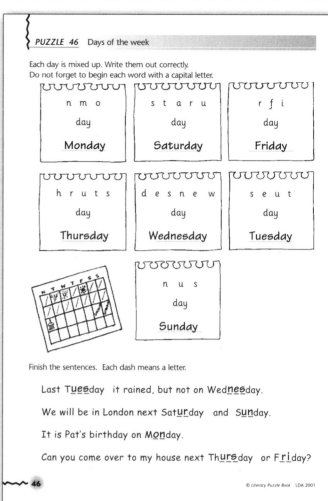

PUZZLE 46 — Days of the week

Each day is mixed up. Write them out correctly.
Do not forget to begin each word with a capital letter.

n m o _ day	s t a r u _ day	r f i _ day
Monday	**Saturday**	**Friday**

h r u t s _ day	d e s n e w _ day	s e u t _ day
Thursday	**Wednesday**	**Tuesday**

n u s _ day
Sunday

Finish the sentences. Each dash means a letter.

Last T**ues**day it rained, but not on Wed**nes**day.

We will be in London next Sat**ur**day and S**un**day.

It is Pat's birthday on M**on**day.

Can you come over to my house next Th**urs**day or F**ri**day?

46

© Literacy Puzzle Book LDA 2001

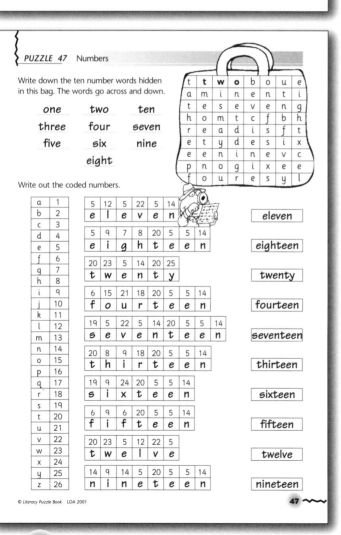

PUZZLE 47 — Numbers

Write down the ten number words hidden in this bag. The words go across and down.

one	two	ten
three	four	seven
five	six	nine
	eight	

Word search grid:

```
t t w o b o u e
a m i n e n t i
t e s e v e n g
h o m t c f b h
r e a d i s f t
e t y d e s i x
e e n i n e v c
p n o g i x e e
f o u r e s y l
```

Write out the coded numbers.

| a 1 | b 2 | c 3 | d 4 | e 5 | f 6 | g 7 | h 8 | i 9 | j 10 | k 11 | l 12 | m 13 | n 14 | o 15 | p 16 | q 17 | r 18 | s 19 | t 20 | u 21 | v 22 | w 23 | x 24 | y 25 | z 26 |

5 12 5 22 5 14 → e l e v e n — eleven

5 9 7 8 20 5 5 14 → e i g h t e e n — eighteen

20 23 5 14 20 25 → t w e n t y — twenty

6 15 21 18 20 5 5 14 → f o u r t e e n — fourteen

19 5 22 5 14 20 5 5 14 → s e v e n t e e n — seventeen

20 8 9 18 20 5 5 14 → t h i r t e e n — thirteen

19 9 24 20 5 5 14 → s i x t e e n — sixteen

6 9 6 20 5 5 14 → f i f t e e n — fifteen

20 23 5 12 22 5 → t w e l v e — twelve

14 9 14 5 20 5 5 14 → n i n e t e e n — nineteen

© Literacy Puzzle Book LDA 2001

47

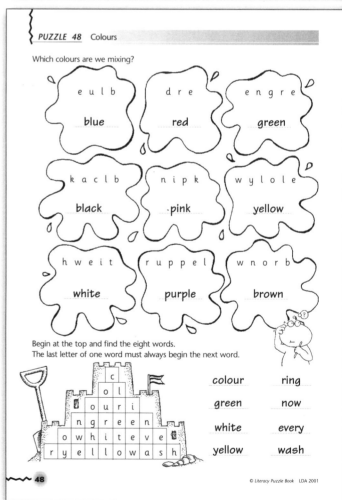

PUZZLE 48 — Colours

Which colours are we mixing?

e u l b — **blue**

d r e — **red**

e n g r e — **green**

k a c l b — **black**

n i p k — **pink**

w y l o l e — **yellow**

h w e i t — **white**

r u p p e l — **purple**

w n o r b — **brown**

Begin at the top and find the eight words.
The last letter of one word must always begin the next word.

```
c
o l
o u r i
n g r e e n
o w h i t e v e
r y e l l o w a s h
```

colour	ring
green	now
white	every
yellow	wash

48

© Literacy Puzzle Book LDA 2001